The Best Of Alex

2019

Charles Peattie

Russell Taylor

Charles Peattie & Russell Taylor

Masterley Publishing

The Best Of
Alex
2019

First Published in 2019 by MASTERLEY PUBLISHING

Layout and Design: Suzette Field

Colouring and Artworking: Sofie Dodgson and Miki Lowe

ISBN: 978-1-5272-4998-1
Printed in the UK by CPI William Clowes Beccles NR34 7TL

FOREWORD

We imagine you are reading this book on Christmas Day, perhaps with a glass of sherry in your hand and a mince pie at your elbow. Forgive this cosy cliché, but it's a commercial reality that the majority of cartoon books are sold in the run up to Christmas. For some of you, we have been told, the Alex annual is up there with the Queen's Broadcast and Brussels Sprouts as an integral part of the festive season.

Christmas is of course is all about the giving and receiving of presents, but this year we ask you to spare a thought for those people who may this Yuletide find themselves deprived of that most precious gift of all: Brexit. For us satirists Brexit has been a godsend. The search engine on our website reveals that since it was first mentioned in the strip in 2014 we have produced 125 cartoons on the subject of Brexit. This tally will no doubt have increased by a dozen or more by the time you are reading these words.

At the time of writing however there is the threat from our Scrooge-like Government to actually implement Brexit on October 31st and thus take away this endless source of free material and force us back into writing jokes about compliance or long lunches instead. In response we can only reaffirm our faith in human nature and trust that our elected representatives in Westminster will hold their nerve and remain as rancorous, fractious and stubborn as ever, fail to agree on anything and decide to defer Brexit yet again, thus allowing it to continue to be the gift that keeps on giving well into the New Year and perhaps the one after too.

But possibly - just possibly - Brexit has actually happened and, if you are a banker, you are reading this book with a glass of Glühwein in your hand and a slice of Stollen and enjoying your very first Christmas in Frankfurt. In which case we'd like to take the opportunity to wish you Fröhliche Weihnachten.

Charles Peattie and Russell Taylor

PENNY   ALEX

CLIVE   RUPERT

JUSTIN   SARA

CYRUS   MEGABANK C.E.O.

SIR STEWART   STEPHANIE

LEO   MILLENNIALS

TRISTRAM

JEREMY BRIDGET VIJAY

9

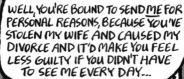

10

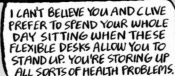

Alex PEATTIE + TAYLOR

ALEX AND CLIVE WERE JUST TELLING ANOTHER STORY ABOUT THE SUPPOSEDLY GOOD OLD DAYS OF THE CITY...

BACK THEN IT SEEMS THAT LIFE WAS A CONSTANT ROUND OF LUNCHING AND CORPORATE ENTERTAINING... AND THEY LOVE TO RUB IT INTO OUR GENERATION WHAT WE MISSED OUT ON...

WELL, I FOR ONE AM GLAD THAT MODERN COMPLIANCE RULES HAVE PUT AN END TO ALL THEIR FUN AND GAMES AND THAT THE CITY IS NOW A MORE SERIOUS BUSINESS - ORIENTED ENVIRONMENT...

BECAUSE IT MIGHT PERSUADE THEM TO FINALLY RETIRE?

QUITE... THEY'D PROBABLY HAVE GONE ON FOR EVER UNDER THE OLD SYSTEM... AND WE'D NEVER BE ABLE TO GET THEIR JOBS...

Alex PEATTIE + TAYLOR

IS IT ME OR ARE PEOPLE IN THE CITY GETTING YOUNGER?

I MEAN, LOOK AT THE ANALYSTS WHO'VE COME IN FOR MY RESULTS PRESENTATION: THEY ALL SEEM SO FRESH-FACED... HARDLY OUT OF SHORT TROUSERS...

IS THIS THE PROCESS OF "JUNIORISATION" IN THE FINANCIAL WORLD THAT I'VE HEARD ABOUT OR AM I JUST SHOWING MY AGE?

PROBABLY A BIT OF BOTH, SIR STEWART...

SO YOU DIDN'T MENTION THAT SINCE MIFID II LOADS OF CITY ANALYSTS HAVE BEEN FIRED AND THERE'S NO ONE LEFT TO WRITE ABOUT HIS COMPANY?

AND THAT WE PADDED OUT HIS PRESENTATION WITH OUR INTERNS? NO FEAR...

Alex PEATTIE + TAYLOR

I REMEMBER BACK IN THE 1980s I'D SOMETIMES DELIBERATELY LEAVE THE PRICE TAG ON A PRESENT I WAS GIVING SOMEONE...

I SUPPOSE IT WAS A SIGN OF IMMATURITY ON OUR PART, CLIVE, BUT BACK IN THOSE MATERIALISTIC TIMES ONE FELT ONE WAS BEING JUDGED BY HOW MUCH ONE SPENT ON THINGS...

YES... ME TOO.

SO I MUST SAY IT'S SAD THAT ALL THESE YEARS ON THERE ARE STILL PEOPLE IN OUR WORLD WHO FEEL OBLIGED TO DRAW ATTENTION TO HOW MUCH A GIFT HAS COST THEM...

"FOR COMPLIANCE PURPOSES THE VALUE OF THIS EVENT IS £49..."

AT LEAST WE WERE TRYING TO BIG UP HOW MUCH STUFF COST, NOT HOW LITTLE...

CORPORATE INVITE

alex@alexcartoon.com

13

Alex FEATTIE + TAYLOR

AND BRIDGET'S GOT A BIG TEAM OF HOTSHOT LAWYERS ON HER SIDE...SHE'S REALLY GOING TO TAKE ME TO THE CLEANERS IN THIS DIVORCE...

SHE'LL GET THE HOUSE, A SHARE OF MY PENSION, NOT TO MENTION A WHOPPING SETTLEMENT. I'LL HAVE TO WORK TILL I'M SEVENTY JUST TO PAY HER OFF...

HEY, LOOK... I'M SORRY TO BANG ON ABOUT ALL THIS... I KNOW YOU DIDN'T CALL TO HEAR ABOUT MY PROBLEMS, BUT THANKS FOR LISTENING...I FEEL SO MUCH BETTER FOR HAVING GOT IT ALL OFF MY CHEST...

WHO WAS THAT?

THE SENIOR ALUMNUS OFFICER FROM MY OLD OXFORD COLLEGE, LOOKING FOR DONATIONS...

HEE HEE... I WON'T BE HEARING FROM HIM AGAIN IN A HURRY...

Alex FEATTIE + TAYLOR

JAMES GOT MADE REDUNDANT FROM THE BANK RECENTLY... HE'S FIFTY-ODD NOW AND IT WAS OVERDUE...

HE'S MANAGED TO GET HIMSELF DESK-SPACE IN SOME LITTLE OFFICE ON THE FRINGES OF THE CITY, AND HE'S BEEN CALLING ROUND EVERYONE IN HIS ADDRESS BOOK TRYING TO GET A MEETING WITH THEM...

HE'S HAVING A DRINK WITH ONE OF HIS CONTACTS WHO'S STILL EMPLOYED AT THE BANK. I'VE BEEN EAVES-DROPPING ON THEIR CONVERSATION... IT'S SAD HEARING A GROWN MAN BEGGING FOR A JOB...

YOU'RE WORKING FOR A "FINTECH" START-UP, JAMES? ER, ANYTHING GOING THERE FOR ME? BANKING IS FINISHED AND I'M DESPERATE TO GET OUT...

ACTUALLY I WANTED YOU TO INVEST IN THE BUSINESS...

Alex FEATTIE + TAYLOR

I CAN'T HELP FEELING BETRAYED WHEN I SEE SO MANY BANKERS WHO GO TO WORK FOR FINTECH START-UPS.

THOSE BLOCKCHAIN AND CRYPTO-CURRENCY COMPANIES WILL DESTROY OUR BUSINESS EVENTUALLY BECAUSE THEY'RE UNDERMINING TRADITIONAL BANKS THAT EMPLOY PEOPLE LIKE YOU AND ME...

OH, BUT, STEVE...

MOST BANKERS WHO JOIN FINTECH COMPANIES ARE OLDER, USELESS ONES WHO GOT FIRED FOR BEING OUT OF TOUCH. THEY WORK UNPAID, THEY JUST NEED PLACES TO GO INTO WORK, WEAR A SUIT AND ARRANGE POINTLESS MEETINGS WITH OLD CONTACTS AS A WAY OF POSTPONING REALITY...

EXACTLY...

...WE OUTPLACEMENT AGENCIES USED TO OFFER THAT SERVICE AND GET PAID FOR IT...

EMPTY

OUT-PLACE-MENT AGENCY

WELL EVERYTHING GETS DISRUPTED EVENTUALLY...

Alex PEATTIE + TAYLOR

LOOK, I APOLOGISE IF YOU THOUGHT I WAS RUDE FOR NOT LOOKING AT YOU WHEN WE WENT PAST EACH OTHER JUST NOW...

FINDING THE RIGHT BALANCE FOR MALE-FEMALE WORKPLACE BEHAVIOUR IS STILL A MINEFIELD FOR CHAPS LIKE ME, EVEN IN THE SPIRIT WORLD...

WHAT I MIGHT BELIEVE TO BE A NATURAL MALE IMPULSE COULD BE SEEN AS A TOTALLY INAPPROPRIATE WAY TO TREAT YOU...

SEE? LIKE, I ALMOST ATTEMPTED TO OPEN THAT DOOR FOR YOU JUST THEN BECAUSE I FORGOT YOU DON'T NEED ME TO, NOW YOU'RE A GHOST...

I WOULDN'T NEED YOU TO DO IT ANYWAY, YOU PATRONISING SEXIST PIG...

≡SIGH≡

Alex PEATTIE + TAYLOR

IT'S NOT JUST ALEX WHO'S DOING "SOBER OCTOBER" YOU KNOW... I'M GOING WITHOUT MY MOJITO IN THE WINE BAR AFTER WORK...

YET HE SEEMS TO BE GETTING ALL THE ATTENTION AND CREDIT. IS IT BECAUSE HE'S OLDER AND BETTER CONNECTED AND CAN RAISE MORE MONEY FOR CHARITY?

IT'S NOT JUST ABOUT THE MONEY, LEO. THIS IS ALSO AN AWARENESS-RAISING CAMPAIGN AND I THINK ALEX IS BETTER SUITED TO THAT TASK.

THE MAITRE D' ALMOST FAINTED WHEN I SPURNED THE WINE LIST...

NO ONE WOULD BAT AN EYELID IF A MILLENNIAL LIKE YOU DIDN'T HAVE A DRINK AT LUNCHTIME...

Alex PEATTIE + TAYLOR

OH DEAR. THE ASTON MARTIN SHARE PRICE HAS COLLAPSED SINCE THE COMPANY WAS FLOATED LAST WEEK...

HARDLY SURPRISING, CLIVE...

IT'S ONLY MADE A PROFIT A COUPLE OF TIMES IN ITS 105-YEAR HISTORY AND HAS GONE BUST SEVEN TIMES. IT'S ENOUGH TO PUT ANY SENSIBLE INVESTOR OFF.

TRUE...

I SUSPECT THE PEOPLE WHO BOUGHT THE SHARES WERE MOTIVATED BY SENTIMENTALITY AND LOVE FOR THE BRAND; BUT I WONDER HOW THEY'LL BE FEELING NOW THEY'VE LOST 10% OF THEIR MONEY...

FINE...

THEY'RE STILL 20% UP ON WHAT THEY'D HAVE LOST IF THEY'D BOUGHT ONE OF THE CARS.

YOU KNOW WHAT HAPPENS TO THE VALUE OF AN UPMARKET VEHICLE AS SOON AS YOU DRIVE IT OFF THE SHOWROOM FORECOURT.

17

Alex PEATTIE + TAYLOR

THE OCTOBER CLUB IS ONE OF THE BIGGEST SOCIAL EVENTS IN THE CITY...

OCTOBER CLUB IN AID OF WELL CHILD

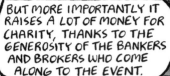

BUT MORE IMPORTANTLY IT RAISES A LOT OF MONEY FOR CHARITY, THANKS TO THE GENEROSITY OF THE BANKERS AND BROKERS WHO COME ALONG TO THE EVENT.

OCTOBER CLUB IN AID OF WELL

BUT OF COURSE WE ARE AWARE THAT THERE'S A LOT OF COMPETITION FOR THEIR MONEY AND THAT OUR REVENUES CAN BE AFFECTED BY RIVAL CHARITABLE FUND-RAISING CAMPAIGNS...

YES...

LIKE "SOBER OCTOBER"...WE NEED PEOPLE BIDDING IN THE AUCTION TO BE WELL-OILED...

LUCKILY ALEX HAS GONE BACK ON THE BOOZE FOR THE EVENING AND HAS PAID OVER THE ODDS FOR EVERY ITEM...

IN AID OF WELL CHILD

Alex PEATTIE + TAYLOR

WE'RE THINKING OF SENDING PHILIP TO FRANKFURT...

BUT THAT WOULD BE HELL FOR HIM. FRANKFURT IS A SOCIAL AND CULTURAL DESERT...

AND LIKE MANY GAY MEN, HE'S A KEEN AFICIONADO OF OPERA, BALLET, THE ARTS... AND HE LOVES SOCIALISING... WHAT'S MORE: HE'S MARRIED TO ANOTHER GAY MAN WHO'S LIKE HIM, SO HE'D HAVE TO GO TOO...

THIS IS TRUE...

SENDING CHAPS LIKE THAT TO FRANKFURT IS A TERRIBLE WASTE... GUYS LIKE THEM NEED TO BE IN LONDON...

SO THEY CAN CARRY ON BEING THE NICE, SAFE GAY-BEST-FRIENDS TO OUR WIVES AND CHAPERONE THEM TO ALL THOSE BORING ARTSY DOS SO THAT WE DON'T HAVE TO GO TO THEM.

AGREED   AGREED.

YES.

Alex PEATTIE + TAYLOR

YOU COMPLIANCE PEOPLE MAKE IT IMPOSSIBLE FOR ORDINARY BANKERS LIKE ME TO DO OUR JOBS...

COMP-LIANCE

EVERY TIME I DO A DEAL I SEEM TO GET CALLED IN BY YOU AND GRILLED TO CHECK I HAVEN'T BROKEN ANY RULES. ARE YOU WAGING A VENDETTA AGAINST ME?

WE'RE JUST DOING OUR JOB. YOU SHOULDN'T TAKE IT SO PERSONALLY...

SO WHAT ABOUT CLIVE THEN? HE NEVER SEEMS TO GET HAULED UP IN FRONT OF YOU.

THAT'S BECAUSE HE NEVER MAKES ANY MONEY...

WHAT?!!

SO IN YOUR BOOK PEOPLE ARE ALWAYS EITHER DISHONEST OR INCOMPETENT? CAN'T YOU EVER CONCEIVE OF ANYONE ACTUALLY BEING GOOD AT THEIR JOB?

NOT UNLESS THEY WORK IN COMPLIANCE, NO...

18

Alex FEATTIE + TAYLOR

CENTRAL BANKS WORLDWIDE ARE BEGINNING TO REVERSE THEIR MONETARY STIMULUS POLICIES...

Q.E. IS OVER AND WE'RE NOW IN THE ERA OF "QUANTITATIVE TIGHTENING" OR Q.T. ... SOME PEOPLE ARE WORRIED BUT I SEE THIS AS A MONEY-MAKING OPPORTUNITY... WE'RE RECRUITING.

I THINK A LITTLE Q.T. IS JUST WHAT WE NEED, AND I SAID AS MUCH IN AN EMAIL TO A CANDIDATE, THOUGH OBVIOUSLY IT'S NOT A CONCEPT THAT'S WELL UNDERSTOOD...

SO IT SEEMS...

NOT BY "AUTO CORRECT" IN ANY CASE. IT CAME OUT AS "A LITTLE CUTIE IS WHAT WE NEED". SHE'S REPORTED ME TO H.R...

THAT'S THE PROBLEM WITH DICTATING YOUR EMAILS INTO YOUR PHONE...

Alex FEATTIE + TAYLOR

THANKS VERY MUCH FOR LUNCH, ALEX. OR RATHER: THANKS TO YOUR BANK...

ACTUALLY I'M PAYING FOR THIS MYSELF...

BUT I'M A CLIENT. I ASSUMED YOU COULD PUT THIS ON EXPENSES.

SADLY NOT... IT'S A WHILE SINCE I'VE SEEN YOU AND COMPLIANCE RULES HAVE BEEN TIGHTENED UP SINCE THEN...

BUT OBVIOUSLY WHEN YOU CALLED YESTERDAY SAYING YOU WERE IN TOWN AND ASKING IF I FANCIED LUNCH I COULD HARDLY SAY NO...

WELL, I'M MOST GRATEFUL...

SO YOU DIDN'T MENTION THAT OUR EXPENSES ARE ACTUALLY LIMITED TO £300 PER CLIENT PER YEAR? AND THAT WE'D ALREADY USED UP HIS ALLOWANCE HAVING AND LUNCH WITH EACH OTHER AND PRETENDING HE WAS THERE? NO...

Alex FEATTIE + TAYLOR

THE BANK'S NEW CORPORATE HEAD-QUARTERS IS SO UNLIKE A TRADITIONAL CITY OFFICE BLOCK...

IT HAS CONCIERGE FACILITIES, HELP DESKS COFFEE FRANCHISES AND COMMUNAL RELAXATION AREAS. THERE'S A REAL EMPHASIS ON SERVICE AND CONVENIENCE.

concierge

IN TERMS OF AMENITIES ON OFFER IT'S LESS LIKE A STUFFY WORKPLACE AND MORE LIKE A HOTEL OR AN AIRPORT LOUNGE WHICH INDICATES HOW A MODERN BANK PERCEIVES ITS WORKFORCE.

YES...

THAT WE'RE ESSENTIALLY IN TRANSIT. WELL THEY'RE GOING TO HAVE TO FIRE LOADS OF US TO PAY FOR ALL OF THIS.

19

24

25

Alex

PEATTIE + TAYLOR

IN THE OLD DAYS WE'D SEND CHRISTMAS CARDS TO EVERYONE WE KNEW IN THE INDUSTRY...

BUT THEN THE BANK STARTED TO WORRY THAT SOME DIFFERENT-FAITH RECIPIENTS MIGHT TAKE OFFENCE AND SO WE HAD TO SEND OUT BLAND SEASON'S GREETINGS MESSAGES, DEVOID OF RELIGIOUS OR HUMOROUS CONTENT.

THEN COST-CUTTING REDUCED US TO ONLY SENDING OUT E-CARDS WHICH DON'T MAKE ANYONE FEEL SPECIAL. IN SHORT THE BANK HAS DESTROYED THE VERY CONCEPT OF THE CHRISTMAS CARD...

TRUE...

SO IT'S PROBABLY FOR THE BEST THAT WE AREN'T ALLOWED TO SEND THEM OUT AT ALL NOW...

YES, BECAUSE IT WOULD INFRINGE G.D.P.R. DATA PROTECTION RULES...

'TIS THE SEASON TO BE VERY AFRAID OF EVERYTHING...

Alex

PEATTIE + TAYLOR

I'VE COMPLETED THE DOCUMENT YOU ASKED FOR, DETAILING MY FINANCES...

THAT'S GOOD, BUT REMEMBER: I'VE BEEN BEFORE THIS JUDGE SEVERAL TIMES. HE HAS A KEEN EYE FOR FIGURES...

SO IF YOU WANT A DECENT FINANCIAL AWARD IN YOUR CASE, DON'T ATTEMPT TO HIDE ANY OF YOUR ASSETS; FRANKLY IT'S BEST TO REVEAL AS MUCH AS POSSIBLE UP FRONT...

OKAY...

HE'LL BE LOOKING VERY CAREFULLY AT YOUR FORM AND HE'LL WANT TO SEE HOW WELL FILLED OUT IT IS...

UNDERSTOOD...

SO WEAR SOMETHING FIGURE-HUGGING AS WELL AS A LOW-CUT TOP

THE JUDGE IS A BIT OF A LETCH, IS HE?

EXACTLY. THEY NEARLY ALL ARE.

Alex

PEATTIE + TAYLOR

FROM A PSYCHOLOGICAL POINT OF VIEW, YOU WANT TO GET THE JUDGE ON YOUR SIDE AND MAKE HIM LOOK KINDLY ON YOU...

THEY TEND TO CLING TO A RATHER OLD-FASHIONED, ROMANTIC IDEA OF THE ABANDONED WIFE IN NEED OF THEIR PROTECTION, SO IT'S BEST TO BE CAUTIOUS ABOUT HOW YOU PRESENT YOUR LIST OF "ESSENTIAL LIFESTYLE REQUIREMENTS."

MAYBE WE SHOULD REMOVE ONE OR TWO ITEMS FROM THIS LIST OF YOUR EXPENSES... THIS BILL FOR YOUR HAIRDRESSER FOR EXAMPLE... IT WON'T HELP YOUR CASE WITH THE JUDGE...

WE DON'T NEED TO LET HIM KNOW YOU COLOUR YOUR HAIR, DO WE? LET HIM MAINTAIN HIS ILLUSIONS...

OKAY

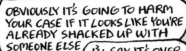

30

31

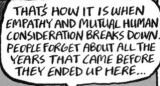

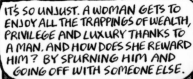

Alex PEATTIE + TAYLOR

WELL, MY DIVORCE HAVING DRAGGED ON FOR THE BEST PART OF TWO YEARS IS FINALLY OVER...

I'M GOING TO HAVE TO PAY A HUGE SETTLEMENT TO BRIDGET, BUT AT LEAST THE WHOLE THING IS DONE AND DUSTED NOW... ALL THE UNCERTAINTIES AND WORRIES ARE BEHIND ME...

I FEEL STRANGELY CONTENTED AND RELAXED... FOR THE FIRST TIME IN A LONG WHILE I CAN LOOK FORWARD TO THE FUTURE WITH OPTIMISM AND CONFIDENCE...

SPEAK FOR YOURSELF. THE REST OF US ARE STILL TERRIFIED OF BEING FIRED IN THE PRE-BONUS ROUND OF REDUNDANCIES.

NOT ME. CYRUS WOULDN'T RISK GETTING RID OF ME AND HAVING TO TAKE OVER THE MAINTENANCE PAYMENTS...

Alex PEATTIE + TAYLOR

SO YOU'RE NOW TAKING THE PROSPECT OF A "NO DEAL" BREXIT MORE SERIOUSLY, CLIVE?

WELL, I STILL THINK IT'S UNLIKELY...

BUT IN VIEW OF THE DIRE WARNINGS AS TO WHAT COULD HAPPEN IN THAT SCENARIO IT'D BE PRUDENT TO LOOK INTO THE POTENTIAL OF OTHER EUROPEAN CITIES AS A BASE FOR THE BANK TO OPERATE OUT OF...

SO I NEED YOU TO BOOK ME URGENT BUSINESS TRIPS TO MILAN, PRAGUE, MADRID AND WARSAW...

OKAY. I UNDERSTAND YOUR FEARS...

THAT PLANES WILL STOP FLYING AFTER MARCH 29TH

RIGHT. AND MY B.A. GOLD CARD COMES UP FOR RENEWAL IN MAY SO I NEED TO GET MY AIR MILES IN BY THEN...

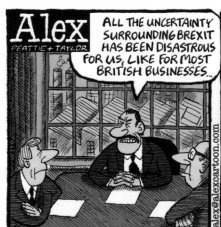

Alex PEATTIE + TAYLOR

ALL THE UNCERTAINTY SURROUNDING BREXIT HAS BEEN DISASTROUS FOR US, LIKE FOR MOST BRITISH BUSINESSES...

AND EVEN NOW, WITH JUST TEN WEEKS TO GO, WE STILL HAVE NO IDEA WHETHER THE U.K. IS FACING CRASHING OUT OF EUROPE WITHOUT A DEAL OR GETTING SOME FORM OF NEGOTIATED SETTLEMENT...

BUT I SPOKE TO OUR CORPORATE ADVISER, ALEX MASTERLEY, TODAY AND HE'S SAID HE'S CONFIDENT THAT EVERYTHING WILL WORK OUT FINE COME MARCH 29TH

OH GOOD...

SO HE RECKONS IT'LL BE NO DEAL? AND TOTAL CHAOS?

YES, SO WE'LL RELEASE OUR DIRE COMPANY RESULTS THAT DAY AS PLANNED...

IT'D BE AWFUL IF ALL WENT SMOOTHLY AND THE MARKET SPOTTED THEM...

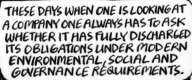

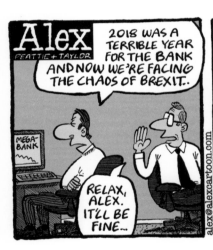

Alex PEATTIE + TAYLOR

SO YOU'RE STILL DRIVING YOUR OLD LAND ROVER DEFENDER, ALEX?

IT'S A MARK OF RESPECTABILITY AND STATUS, CLIVE...

PLUS IT SHOWS THAT I CAN AFFORD TO PAY THIS NEW DIESEL TAX...

MAYBE, BUT WHAT ABOUT THE ENVIRONMENTAL CONSEQUENCES?

MANY PEOPLE ARE NOW GETTING RID OF THESE GAS-GUZZLING BEHEMOTHS DUE TO THE HIGH LEVELS OF TOXIC EMISSIONS AND GREENHOUSE GASES THAT THEY PRODUCE. AREN'T YOU WORRIED ABOUT THAT?

OH YES...

IT'S CAUSED THE MARKET TO BE FLOODED WITH CUT-PRICE, SECOND-HAND LAND ROVERS. I JUST HOPE NO ONE THINKS THAT I'M DRIVING ONE OF THEM...

Alex PEATTIE + TAYLOR

I WORRY ABOUT MILLENNIALS LIKE LEO. THEY'RE SO DIFFERENT FROM US BABY BOOMERS

I MEAN, OUR GENERATION TENDS TO HAVE A MORE ORIGINAL, INDEPENDENT, QUESTIONING OUTLOOK; WHEREAS THE MILLENNIALS ARE OF A MORE CONFORMIST MINDSET WHICH IS BLANDLY ACCEPTING OF THE STATUS QUO...

SO WHEN IT COMES TO WINNING BUSINESS IT'S VERY CLEAR WHICH OF US IS GOING TO OFFER CLIENTS THE ADDED VALUE THAT THEY REQUIRE...

I LIKE LEO: HE TELLS ME WHAT I WANT TO HEAR AND DOESN'T OBSTRUCT MY EMPIRE-BUILDING WITH BORING NIT-PICKING AND NAY-SAYING...

WELL, YOU WON'T BE C.E.O. FOR LONG AND YOU WANT TO RAKE IN AS MUCH MONEY AS YOU CAN...

Alex PEATTIE + TAYLOR

I WISH CLIVE WOULD STOP PLAYING THE VICTIM TO THE KIDS ABOUT HOW HE'S TOO POOR TO AFFORD TO BUY THEM THINGS...

HE DOES IT DELIBERATELY BECAUSE HE KNOWS THEY'LL RELAY IT TO ME. IT'S HIS WAY OF GUILT-TRIPPING ME ABOUT SUPPOSEDLY FLEECING HIM IN THE DIVORCE.

SPURIOUSLY CLAIMING POVERTY?

EXACTLY.

SO BASICALLY HE'S USING THE CHILDREN TO COMMUNICATE INDIRECTLY TO THE PARENT ON THE OTHER SIDE, SO AS TO GET THE MESSAGE ACROSS THAT HE'S GOT NO MONEY?

IT'S A COMMON PSYCHO-LOGICAL PLOY, CYRUS...

WOW.

PING!

ACCORDING TO MY KIDS, CYRUS CAN'T AFFORD COURCHEVEL THIS YEAR AND IS TAKING THEM SKIING IN BULGARIA INSTEAD...

NOT STRICTLY TRUE, BUT EFFECTIVE...

OH GOD. BONUSES MUST BE GOING TO BE REALLY LOW...

41

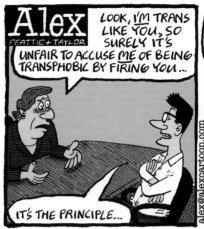

Alex PEATTIE + TAYLOR

WITH GREATER LIFE EXPECTANCY, UNDER-FUNDED PENSIONS AND GENERAL INDEBTEDNESS, PEOPLE THESE DAYS ARE NEEDING TO WORK LONGER.

AND OF COURSE MODERN RULES ON AGEISM PREVENT EMPLOYERS FROM BEING ABLE TO STIPULATE A RETIREMENT AGE ON JOB CONTRACTS...

ALL OF WHICH HAS HAD A SIGNIFICANT EFFECT ON HOW LONG OUR MORE SENIOR STAFF END UP STAYING IN THEIR JOBS FOR...

YES...

ONCE UPON A TIME JIM WOULD HAVE GOT A COUPLE MORE YEARS HERE WHILE WE WAITED UNTIL WE COULD PENSION HIM OFF.

QUITE. BUT AS THAT'S NOT GOING TO HAPPEN WE MIGHT AS WELL BITE THE BULLET AND FIRE HIM NOW.

Alex PEATTIE + TAYLOR

SO YOU'RE DOING YOUR USUAL TRIP WITH YOUR RUGBY MATES TO THE WORLD CUP IN THE AUTUMN, ALEX? WHERE IS IT BEING HELD?

JAPAN...

REALLY? DO YOU KNOW I'VE NEVER BEEN TO JAPAN, BUT IT'S SOMEWHERE I'VE ALWAYS WANTED TO GO. THE CULTURE AND FOOD THERE IS BEAUTIFUL...

THE BULLET TRAIN IS SUPPOSED TO BE AN AMAZING EXPERIENCE AND I HEAR MOUNT FUJI IS BREATHTAKING...

ALL RIGHT, PENNY. SAY NO MORE. YOU'VE GOT YOUR HOLIDAY...

SO, WHERE DO YOU WANT TO GO?

THE CARIBBEAN, PLEASE. NEXT WINTER. THAT'S THE TRADE OFF FOR ME **NOT** TO COME WITH YOU ON YOUR SADDO, LADS-ONLY, MALE-BONDING, BOOZY RUGBY SHINDIG.

YOU DRIVE A HARD BARGAIN...

Alex PEATTIE + TAYLOR

THESE DAYS LINKED-IN IS THE PRIME SOURCE OF INFORMATION ON PEOPLE IN THE BUSINESS WORLD...

WHENEVER YOU'VE DONE SOMETHING NEW OR SPECIAL IT SENDS OUT AN EMAIL TO EVERYONE YOU'RE CONNECTED WITH, HELPING BOOST YOUR PROFESSIONAL KUDOS IN THEIR EYES.

BUT OF COURSE THE DETAILS OF CAREERS AND ACHIEVEMENTS THAT PEOPLE LAY CLAIM TO ARE NOT ALWAYS STRICTLY ACCURATE. SOMETIMES THEY TAKE A FEW LIBERTIES WITH FACTS AND DATES.

"Congratulate Alex Masterley for 14 years at Megabank"

ER, SURELY IT'S MUCH LONGER THAN THAT, ALEX?

SHH... I DON'T WANT OUR BOSSES THINKING I'M GETTING LONG IN THE TOOTH AND RIPE TO BE FIRED...

45

Alex PEATTIE + TAYLOR

PEOPLE ARE SAYING THAT THERE ARE MANY SIMILARITIES BETWEEN NOW AND THE FINANCIAL CRISIS OF 2007-2008...

THAT BANKS ARE UNDERWRITING LOANS TO RISKY COMPANIES AND PACKAGING THEM UP INTO COMPLEX DERIVATIVE PRODUCTS VERY LIKE THE ONES THAT WENT WRONG BACK THEN...

WE'D BE STUPID NOT TO HAVE LEARNT OUR LESSON, CLIVE...

NOWADAYS THERE ARE MANY MORE CHECKS AND BALANCES IN PLACE AND BANKS ARE FAR MORE AWARE OF THE DANGERS OF SUCH A SITUATION...

WHAT, OF HOLDING THAT TOXIC RUBBISH ON OUR OWN BOOKS?

QUITE. SO WE'RE MAKING SURE WE SELL IT ALL ON TO THE PENSION FUNDS...

LET THEM TAKE THE HIT WHEN IT ALL BLOWS UP AGAIN...

Alex PEATTIE + TAYLOR

IT'S VERY DIFFICULT HAVING ONE'S PERSONAL LIFE MIXED UP WITH ONE'S WORKING LIFE...

I MEAN, I'M ROMANTICALLY INVOLVED WITH CLIVE'S EX-WIFE, WHICH MAKES CERTAIN THINGS SOMEWHAT COMPLICATED FOR MY RELATIONSHIP WITH HIM HERE AT THE OFFICE...

AS HIS BOSS I CAN'T SIMPLY LET HIM KNOW WHAT I THINK OF HIM AS I MIGHT LIKE TO, REVEALING THE DEPTH OF MY UTTER CONTEMPT FOR HIM AS A PERSON...

THAT MUST BE FRUSTRATING...

YOU KNOW, YOU REALLY _ARE_ CRAP AT YOUR JOB, CLIVE. THAT'S WHY I'M GIVING YOU SUCH A SMALL BONUS... IT'S GOT NOTHING TO DO WITH OUR PRIVATE FEUD...

YES, BUT YOU _WOULD_ SAY THAT, WOULDN'T YOU?

DELUDED COMPLACENCY

GRRR...

Alex PEATTIE + TAYLOR

CLIVE IS GRUMBLING ABOUT YOU GIVING HIM A SMALL BONUS, CYRUS...

HE JUST WANTS TO MAKE HIMSELF OUT TO BE A VICTIM, BRIDGET...

HE CAN'T GET OVER THE FACT THAT YOU AND I ARE NOW IN A RELATIONSHIP...

ACTUALLY HE ALWAYS GRUMBLED ABOUT HIS BONUS WHEN HE AND I WERE STILL MARRIED...

BUT I FELT DIFFERENTLY IN THOSE DAYS. EVEN THOUGH WE DIDN'T HAVE THE GREATEST MARRIAGE, HE WAS MY MAN AND I ALWAYS WANTED TO THINK THE BEST OF HIM.

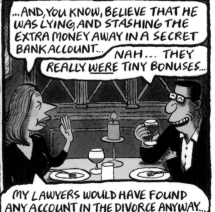

...AND, YOU KNOW, BELIEVE THAT HE WAS LYING, AND STASHING THE EXTRA MONEY AWAY IN A SECRET BANK ACCOUNT...

NAH... THEY REALLY _WERE_ TINY BONUSES...

MY LAWYERS WOULD HAVE FOUND ANY ACCOUNT IN THE DIVORCE ANYWAY...

48

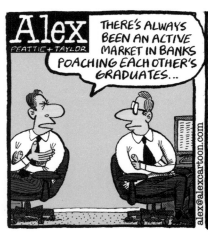

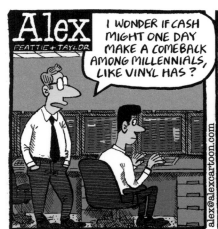

51

54

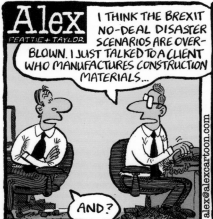

Panel 1: WE SENIOR PEOPLE SEEM TO GET IN TO THE OFFICE EARLIER THAN OUR MILLENNIAL JUNIORS...

Panel 2: I THINK THERE'S SOMETHING SERIOUSLY WRONG WITH THEIR WORK ETHIC...

NO, THEY JUST LIKE TO GO TO THE GYM BEFORE WORK IN THE MORNING..

Panel 3: PERHAPS IT'S <u>YOU</u> WHO'S OUT OF TOUCH WITH THE MODERN CITY ETHOS WHICH IS ABOUT WORK-LIFE BALANCE AND REALISING JUST BECAUSE WE DO A SEDENTARY JOB, IT DOESN'T MEAN WE CAN'T BE FIT, LIMBER AND AGILE.

LISTEN: I AM <u>VERY</u> CONCERNED WITH AGILITY.

Panel 4: NAMELY THIS BLASTED "AGILE WORKING" REGIME, WHEREBY YOU NEED TO GET IN FIRST TO ENSURE YOU GET THE BEST DESK...

BAD LUCK, LEO. I SAW IT FIRST...

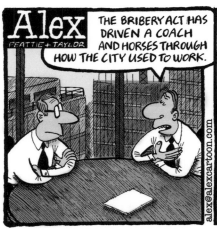

Panel 1: THE BRIBERY ACT HAS DRIVEN A COACH AND HORSES THROUGH HOW THE CITY USED TO WORK.

Panel 2: COMPLIANCE IS CRACKING DOWN ON INDUCEMENTS WHICH HAS MEANT A MAJOR OVERHAUL IN THE WAY WE APPOINT OUR SERVICE PROVIDERS LIKE PRINTERS...

Panel 3: WE NOW ASSESS THE INDIVIDUAL MERITS OF EACH PRINTING COMPANY PROPERLY AND OBJECTIVELY, AND I MUST SAY IT'S BEEN VERY INFORMATIVE...

YES...

Panel 4: FRANKLY THEY'RE ALL MUCH OF A MUCHNESS..

QUITE. PROVING WE WERE RIGHT IN THE OLD DAYS JUST TO NOT BOTHER WITH ANY COMPARATIVE ANALYSIS OTHER THAN WHO'D TAKE US ON SKIING TRIPS TO VERBIER.

AND GIVE OUR BUSINESS TO <u>THEM</u>, YES.

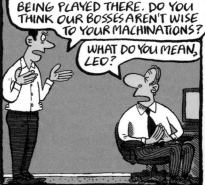

Panel 1: SO YOU'RE GOING ON AN ALL-EXPENSES-PAID BUSINESS TRIP TO HONG KONG, ALEX?

Panel 2: COINCIDENTALLY IN THE SAME WEEK THAT THE RUGBY SEVENS ARE BEING PLAYED THERE. DO YOU THINK OUR BOSSES AREN'T WISE TO YOUR MACHINATIONS?

WHAT DO YOU MEAN, LEO?

Panel 3: I MEAN, YOU'VE SET UP A FEW TOKEN CLIENT MEETINGS OUT THERE. BUT ESSENTIALLY YOU'RE GETTING THE BANK TO PAY FOR YOU TO WATCH SPORT.

REALLY, LEO, THAT'S VERY DISRESPECTFUL OF YOU...

Panel 4: I'M ACTUALLY GETTING THE BANK TO PAY FOR ME TO FIND MYSELF A NEW JOB. I'VE ALSO SET UP A LOAD OF HEADHUNTER MEETINGS.

THERE'S NO BREXIT OR MIFID II OUT THERE.

SOUNDS GOOD.

57

58

Panel 1: PEOPLE OFTEN ASK ME WHAT IS THE SECRET OF MY LONGEVITY IN THE CITY...

Panel 2: THE TRICK IS TO KEEP YOURSELF RELEVANT IN THESE CHALLENGING TIMES. OURS IS A "PEOPLE" BUSINESS. IT'S ALL ABOUT WHO YOU KNOW...

Panel 3: WHICH IS WHY I'VE ALWAYS KEPT A COMPREHENSIVE ADDRESS BOOK WITH DETAILS OF ALL THE CONTACTS I'VE MADE OVER THE COURSE OF MY CAREER.

Panel 4: AND NOW HARDLY A DAY PASSES WITHOUT ONE OF THEM PHONING AND BEGGING ME FOR A JOB... ≷SIGH≷ IT'S A DIFFERENT WORLD NOW OUR GENERATION HAS MOSTLY BEEN CULLED... ≷RING RING≷ I MIGHT AS WELL BIN THE BOOK...

Panel 1: THIS RESTAURANT IS ALWAYS HALF EMPTY THESE DAYS... THAT'S WHY WE'RE LOSING MONEY.

Panel 2: BACK IN THE 80S AND 90S WHEN PEOPLE HAD PROPER EXPENSE ACCOUNTS AND BEFORE THEY HAD ISSUES WITH COMPLIANCE WE'D BE FULL EVERY LUNCHTIME...

Panel 3: I'D REGULARLY CASH UP AND FIND WE'D DONE 100 COVERS IN A SINGLE SITTING AT LUNCHTIME. ER, BUT, ANTONIO, THE RESTAURANT ONLY SEATS 60... EXACTLY...

Panel 4: PEOPLE WOULD GET ME TO PUT EXTRA "CLIENTS" DOWN ON THEIR BILL TO JUSTIFY ALL THE BOOZE THEY'D GOT THROUGH... THOSE WERE THE DAYS...

Panel 1: EUROPE HAS ALWAYS BEEN THE BANK'S PRIME BUSINESS MARKET, BUT THIS COULD VANISH POST-BREXIT...

Panel 2: THERE'S NO POINT IN FRETTING ABOUT IT, CLIVE... WE SHOULD LOOK ON THIS AS AN OPPORTUNITY RATHER THAN A PROBLEM. FOCUS ON DEVELOPING OUR BUSINESS FURTHER AFIELD...

Panel 3: THE MIDDLE EAST, ASIA, THE AMERICAS, AFRICA... THERE'S THE WHOLE OF THE REST OF THE WORLD OUT THERE AND IT HAS A LOT TO OFFER... YOU'RE RIGHT...

Panel 4: BUSINESS CLASS TRAVEL, WHICH WE'RE ONLY ALLOWED TO TAKE ON FLIGHTS OF OVER 5 HOURS. AT LEAST WE SHOULD GET SOME AIR MILES OUT OF THIS DEBACLE...

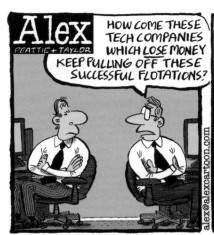

65

Alex
PEATTIE + TAYLOR

WHAT?! YOU ADMIRE THE BREXIT PARTY?! BUT THEY DON'T EVEN BELIEVE IN THE PARLIAMENT THEY'RE TRYING TO GET ELECTED TO...

WE CAN ALL LEARN FROM THEM, CYRUS

THEY DON'T LIKE THIS REMOTE, MONOLITHIC INSTITUTION IN EUROPE BUT IF THEY GET APPOINTED TO IT THEY'LL GO THERE AND THEY'LL TAKE THE SALARIES AND THE PERKS...

AND THEN THEY'LL SET ABOUT WORKING TO BE THE MOST AWKWARD DISRUPTIVE MEMBERS OF THE ORGANISATION THEY CAN BE, HOPING TO BRING IT DOWN FROM THE INSIDE BY CAUSING AS MUCH TROUBLE AS POSSIBLE UNTIL THEY GET SENT HOME...

JEEZ!

WHAT THE HECK KIND OF EXAMPLE IS THAT SETTING?

ER, WE-ELL...

PLINK   PENNY DROPS

OH. OKAY... YOU'RE OFF THE FRANKFURT TRANSFER LIST, ALEX.

THANK YOU!

Alex
PEATTIE + TAYLOR

THE UNCERTAINTY AND INDECISION ABOUT BREXIT IS PARALYSING OUR BUSINESS...

NONE OF THE BANK'S CLIENTS WILL DO ANY DEALS UNTIL THEY HAVE A CLEAR PICTURE OF WHETHER WE'LL STILL BE IN THE E.U. IN THE FUTURE OR NOT... WE NEED THIS ISSUE SETTLED.

FRUSTRATINGLY THE CONDITIONS FOR GETTING COMPANIES TO ENGAGE IN BUSINESS ARE ACTUALLY VERY FAVOURABLE AT THE MOMENT.

WHAT, HEALTHY ECONOMIC GROWTH AND LOW INFLATION..?

NO, THE IMMINENT PROSPECT OF A LABOUR GOVERNMENT. THAT'S USUALLY A GOOD WAY FOR US TO SCARE THEM INTO DOING SOME DEALS WHILE THEY STILL HAVE THE CHANCE

GRR...

Alex
PEATTIE + TAYLOR

SO DONALD TRUMP HAS BANNED SALES OF TECHNOLOGY TO HUAWEI?

TRADE WAR

YES. IT'S GOOD THAT HE'S RAISING AWARENESS OF THESE INHERENT DANGERS, CLIVE...

LET'S FACE IT, WE'RE UP AGAINST A RUTHLESS AND CYNICAL ADVERSARY THAT IS ACTIVELY WORKING AGAINST OUR COMMERCIAL INTERESTS BY CONDUCTING LISTENING OPERATIONS AGAINST US...

IT'S A NEW COLD WAR, CLIVE. IT HASN'T BEEN OPENLY DECLARED YET, BUT WE ALL KNOW WHO THE ENEMY IS... IT BEGINS WITH A 'C'...

COMPLIANCE?

EXACTLY. AND AT LEAST NOW THEY CAN'T IMPOSE THOSE CHEAPO SMARTPHONES ON US AS PART OF THE BANK'S COST-CUTTING DRIVE...

66

WITH A NO-DEAL BREXIT NOW LOOKING MORE LIKELY, THE BANK IS SPEEDING UP ITS FRANKFURT RELOCATION PLANS.

WE HAVE TO RESIST THIS MOVE VIGOROUSLY, CLIVE... REMIND OUR BOSSES THAT THE U.K. IS STILL THE PLACE IN EUROPE WHERE PEOPLE WANT TO DO BUSINESS...

WE JUST HAVE TO SHOW THEM THAT OUR DIARIES ARE CHOCK-A-BLOCK WITH INTERNATIONAL CLIENTS WHO ARE CHOOSING TO COME HERE TO THE U.K., NOT TO CONTINENTAL EUROPE.

ER, COULD THAT BE BECAUSE THE CRICKET WORLD CUP STARTS HERE THIS WEEK?

HMM... MAYBE WE SHOULDN'T MENTION THAT THEY'RE MAINLY FROM AUSTRALIA, NEW ZEALAND AND SOUTH AFRICA...

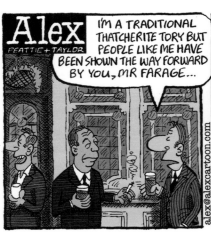

I'M A TRADITIONAL THATCHERITE TORY BUT PEOPLE LIKE ME HAVE BEEN SHOWN THE WAY FORWARD BY YOU, MR FARAGE...

YOU'RE A WINNER, AND YOU DID IT BY ESCHEWING THE OLD, OUTDATED INSTITUTIONAL MODES OF THE PAST.. I'VE ACTUALLY HAD TO QUESTION MY OLD CERTAINTIES... IT'S BEEN UNSETTLING...

AS SOON AS I SAW YOU STARTING YOUR CAMPAIGNING FOR THE BREXIT PARTY, I THOUGHT: "NOW HERE IS A POLITICIAN OF A DIFFERENT STRIPE..."

AH YES...

THAT WAS MY IMAGE CONSULTANT. SHE SAID, "DITCH THE TRADEMARK PINSTRIPE SUIT THIS TIME, NIGE..."

I'M HAVING A CRISIS OF SELF-CONFIDENCE ABOUT MINE NOW...

SO YOU THINK IT'S A GOOD DECISION OF MINE TO TAKE MY IDEOLOGICAL LEAD FROM NIGEL FARAGE?

I APPLAUD IT, YES..

THIS WHOLE BREXIT ISSUE HAS UPSET THE POLITICAL APPLECART IN THIS COUNTRY... WHICH WILL EVENTUALLY SEND US ALL IN A COMPLETELY NEW DIRECTION...

INDEED.

THE ONLY QUESTION I HAVE IS: TO THE LEFT OR TO THE RIGHT?

ER...

OH, THE LEFT PLEASE, IF YOU'RE MEASURING MY INSIDE LEG...

SO HOW MANY OF THESE NEW NON-PINSTRIPE SUITS WILL YOU REQUIRE, MR MASTERLEY?

2 PLEASE, BUT 3 TROUSERS...

GOOD DECISION, SIR. I WISH I HAD MORE CUSTOMERS LIKE YOU...

Alex PEATTIE + TAYLOR

THANKS FOR INVITING ME TO DINNER AT YOUR HOUSE LAST WEEK, ALISTAIR...

IT WAS FUN, SEAN...

BUT YOU NEED TO LEARN TO CHILL OUT MORE. THAT WAS PURELY A SOCIAL OCCASION. YOU DIDN'T NEED TO LOG IT WITH YOUR BANK AS A FORMAL "CLIENT INTERACTION".

SORRY, ALISTAIR...

I JUST WANTED TO SHOW MY BOSS HOW HARD I'M WORKING. AFTER ALL, THINGS ARE TOUGH FOR US ANALYSTS NOW WE HAVE ALL THESE MIFID II RULES...

IT AFFECTS ALL OF US...

I'VE JUST RECEIVED THIS BILL FROM YOUR BANK FOR £4,000 FOR TWO HOURS OF YOUR TIME. WE CLIENTS HAVE TO PAY FOR THAT, REMEMBER.

OOPS...

Alex PEATTIE + TAYLOR

HOW EXCITING HAVING THE CRICKET WORLD CUP IN THIS COUNTRY AS WELL AS ASCOT, WIMBLEDON, AND HENLEY...

AND WITH THE BANK HAVING NO BUSINESS ON UNTIL BREXIT IS SORTED IT'S EASY TO SLIP AWAY TO ENJOY IT WITHOUT HAVING TO USE UP ONE'S HOLIDAY ALLOWANCE...

IT'S ALL VERY WELL TO TALK ABOUT SPENDING THE SUMMER WATCHING SPORT, ALEX, BUT WHAT ABOUT THE AUTUMN WHEN WE'RE FACING THE PROSPECT OF A NO DEAL BREXIT ON OCTOBER 31ST?

AH YES...

I'LL BE AWAY IN JAPAN FOR THE RUGBY WORLD CUP FINAL ON NOVEMBER 2ND... I'VE ALREADY GOT MY LEAVE BOOKED.

I'LL MISS ALL THE MARKET CARNAGE... EVEN BETTER...

Alex PEATTIE + TAYLOR

I CAN'T BELIEVE THAT A CLIENT HAD THE TEMERITY TO CALL US IN FOR A MEETING ON A FRIDAY AFTERNOON...

BUT, ALEX, IT'S A VALID PART OF OUR WORKING WEEK... CLIENTS HAVE A RIGHT TO CALL ON OUR TIME.

MAYBE, LEO

BUT IN THE OLD DAYS THEY WOULD EXERCISE A DUE SENSE OF CONSIDERATION. WHAT, YOU NEVER SCHEDULED MEETINGS FOR A FRIDAY AFTERNOON?

OF COURSE WE DID.

BUT THEY WERE BOGUS ONES-PUT IN THE DIARY SO THAT THE CLIENT AND I COULD BOTH SLIP OFF EARLY FOR THE WEEKEND...

WHICH IS WHAT I THOUGHT THIS WAS UNTIL I GOT A CALL FROM HIS P.A. ASKING WHERE I WAS...

Alex PEATTIE + TAYLOR

IT'S ASTONISHING... MICHAEL GOVE, LIKE SEVERAL OTHER TORY LEADERSHIP CANDIDATES HAS ADMITTED TO TRYING CLASS 'A' DRUGS...

APPARENTLY WHEN HE WAS YOUNGER HE TOOK COCAINE AS A RESULT OF HIS SOCIAL LIFE, BUT NOW REGRETS IT...

IT'S HARD TO BELIEVE HE'D BE SO FOOLISH. COCAINE IS A SERIOUS DRUG. WHY WOULD ANY POLITICIAN TAKE THE RISK TO THEIR CAREER WHEN YOU THINK OF THE EFFECT IT WOULD HAVE?

WHAT, LIKE MAKING THEM GABBLE AWAY WITH SUPREME SELF-CONFIDENCE FOR HOURS ON END WITHOUT ANY AWARENESS OF HOW BORING THEY'RE BEING? THAT'S NOT NECESSARILY A DRAWBACK FOR A POLITICIAN...

BUT THE DRUGS SEEM LIKE A WASTE OF MONEY.

Alex PEATTIE + TAYLOR

SO NEIL WOODFORD'S FUND WAS POSITIONED TO TAKE ADVANTAGE OF A NICE STRAIGHTFORWARD BREXIT?

THAT WAS THE PROBLEM, YES...

BUT I DON'T THINK ANYONE HAD FORESEEN HOW HARD IT WOULD BE TO LEAVE. OR HOW THERE WOULD BE PEOPLE WHO WOULD DO ANYTHING IN THEIR POWER TO PREVENT IT FROM HAPPENING...

I SUPPOSE THEY DO IT "POUR ENCOURAGER LES AUTRES", BECAUSE THEY FEAR THAT IF ANYONE IS ALLOWED TO EXIT, THEN OTHERS WILL FOLLOW SUIT AND BRING THE WHOLE EDIFICE TUMBLING DOWN.

OH WELL. THAT'S THE E.U. FOR YOU.

ACTUALLY I WAS TALKING ABOUT NEIL WOODFORD'S FUND. GETTING OUT OF EUROPE SHOULD BE A DODDLE IN COMPARISON...

Alex PEATTIE + TAYLOR

SO MANY INVESTORS ARE PUTTING THEIR MONEY INTO PASSIVE, INDEX TRACKING FUNDS THESE DAYS, ALEX.

YOU CAN HARDLY BLAME THEM, LIAM.

HUMAN FUND MANAGERS LIKE YOU CHARGE BIG FEES FOR YOUR SUPPOSED EXPERTISE AND YOU CAN'T EVEN BEAT THE INDEX...

MAYBE, BUT THIS IS A DANGEROUS SITUATION.

IF ALL FUNDS BECAME PASSIVE FUNDS THAT MERELY TRACK THE INDEX, IT WOULD LEAD TO DISTORTED MARKETS AND ANOMALIES IN SHARE PRICES...

INDEED...

WHICH WOULD CREATE A DEMAND FOR _ACTIVE_ FUND MANAGERS LIKE YOU TO EXPLOIT ALL THOSE OPPORTUNITIES...

IF YOU'RE ANY GOOD AT YOUR JOB, THAT IS...

AH...

ER...

71

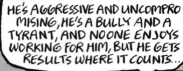

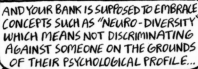

Alex

PEATTIE + TAYLOR

THAT WAS A SHORT MEETING WITH YOUR BANKERS, SIR STEWART.

WELL THEY WERE WASTING MY TIME AS USUAL...

THEY ONLY KEEP COMING UP HERE BECAUSE THEY'RE TRYING TO SHOW THEIR BANK THAT THEY HAVE U.K.-BASED CLIENTS, SO THEY DON'T GET SENT TO WORK IN FRANKFURT, POST-BREXIT...

I REMINDED THEM THAT I WON'T BE DOING ANY DEALS UNTIL BREXIT IS SORTED AND SENT THEM PACKING, SO THEY CAME ALL THE WAY TO YORKSHIRE FOR NOTHING...

PERFECT... A NICE SHORT MEETING AND WE GOT TO HEADINGLEY FOR THE START OF THE CRICKET.

YES, WITH THE WHOLE DAY SIGNED OFF FROM WORK.

CRICKET WORLD CUP

BLISS!

Alex

PEATTIE + TAYLOR

SO YOU'VE BEEN WORKING OUT HERE IN FRANKFURT A WHOLE YEAR? BAD LUCK... I JUST ARRIVED LAST MONTH.

ACTUALLY PEOPLE LIKE ME WHO WERE SENT HERE BY OUR BANKS IN THE FIRST WAVE DID BETTER THAN YOU RECENT ARRIVALS. WE GOT MORE GENEROUS RELOCATION PACKAGES.

NOT ONLY DID I GET MY BONUS GUARANTEED, BUT I HAVE AN ACCOMMODATION ALLOWANCE, PLUS REGULAR FREE FLIGHTS HOME, WHICH IS WHAT I'M AVAILING MYSELF OF NOW.

LUCKY YOU. WHAT ARE YOU GOING TO DO IN LONDON?

A JOB INTERVIEW. I'M DESPERATE TO GET OUT OF THIS PLACE...

ME TOO.

BUT, UNLIKE YOU, MY TRIP IS BEING PAID FOR BY MY CURRENT EMPLOYER.

HOPE WE'RE NOT UP FOR THE SAME JOB, EH?

Alex

PEATTIE + TAYLOR

HERE'S A LIST OF ALL THE PEOPLE I'D LIKE TO INVITE TO MY DINNER PARTY NEXT WEEK...

PML FAMILY SOLICITORS

THEY'RE ALL FORMER CLIENTS OF YOURS, JEREMY...

YES. AS A DIVORCE LAWYER I DEAL WITH A LOT OF UNHAPPY, DISTRESSED PEOPLE WHO HAVE COME OUT OF LONG MARRIAGES AND SUDDENLY FIND THEMSELVES NEWLY SINGLE, OFTEN IN MIDDLE AGE...

THESE DINNERS GIVE ME THE CHANCE TO DO SOMETHING POSITIVE TO ALLOW THESE PEOPLE TO REGAIN THEIR SOCIAL CONFIDENCE. MAYBE MEET SOMEONE NEW. WHO KNOWS WHAT IT MIGHT LEAD TO?

MARRIAGE?

YES...

HOPEFULLY FOLLOWED BY DIVORCE A FEW YEARS DOWN THE LINE...

WELL YOU NEED TO GET YOURSELF SOME REPEAT BUSINESS...

IT'S JUST A SHAME I WON'T BE ABLE TO REPRESENT BOTH PARTIES...

Alex
PEATTIE + TAYLOR

SO YOU'RE TAKING AN ECO-FRIENDLY COACH TO GLASTONBURY INSTEAD OF A CAR, LEO? MOST IMPRESSIVE...

WELL, THE FESTIVAL IS ENCOURAGING GREEN TRAVEL, BUT TO BE HONEST I ONLY WENT FOR THE COACH OPTION BECAUSE IT INCLUDED A TICKET TO THE FESTIVAL AND THEY WERE TOTALLY SOLD OUT OTHERWISE..

I SEE...

I'D BE A HYPOCRITE IF I TRIED TO PRETEND I WAS DOING IT FOR PURELY ECOLOGICAL REASONS...

WELL, I ADMIRE YOU FOR THAT.

HE'D ADMIRE YOU EVEN MORE IF HE KNEW THAT THE ONLY AVAILABLE COACH IS FROM GLASGOW AND YOU'RE HAVING TO FLY UP FROM LONDON TO CATCH IT...*

THAT'S TOO MUCH HYPOCRISY TO ADMIT TO...

* (TRUE STORY)

alex@alexcartoon.com

Alex
PEATTIE + TAYLOR

WHAT? YOU'RE ON YOUR WAY TO GLASTONBURY TOO, ALEX?

THAT'S RIGHT, I SEE IT AS PART OF THE SOCIAL SEASON THESE DAYS, LEO

COACH

alex@alexcartoon.com

IT'S IMPORTANT TO SHOW ONE'S FACE AT THESE OCCASIONS, MEET THE RIGHT PEOPLE THERE AND MAINTAIN ONE'S NETWORK OF CONNECTIONS...

WOW. OKAY, BUT I NEVER THOUGHT YOU WERE THE TYPE FOR BEING "DOWN WITH THE KIDS"..

I'M NOT..

I WOULDN'T WANT TO BE DOWN THERE WITH YOU LOT. IT LOOKS LIKE GRIDLOCK...

I PREFER TO BE UP HERE WITH THE HEDGE FUNDERS...PLUS THE V.I.P. AREA LATER OF COURSE...

HONK   HONK   HONK

Alex
PEATTIE + TAYLOR

SOME OF OUR STAFF ARE UNHAPPY ABOUT THE BANK MOVING ITS OPERATIONS TO FRANKFURT POST BREXIT...

YES...

alex@alexcartoon.com

FRANKFURT IS A MUCH SMALLER FINANCIAL CENTRE THAN LONDON AND QUITE A FEW PEOPLE HAVE RESIGNED RATHER THAN HAVE TO GO AND WORK THERE ...

WELL, THAT'S SAVED THE BANK SOME MONEY.

TRUE, BUT WE NEED TO ACT WITH CONSIDERATION WITH REGARD TO THE PEOPLE WHO HAVE AGREED TO GO; TO ENSURE THAT THEY ARE INTEGRATED AND ASSIMILATED OUT THERE AS QUICKLY AS POSSIBLE...

YES...

BY "REBASING" THEIR SALARIES AND BONUSES TO REFLECT "LOCAL MARKET NORMS"..

HEE HEE...WHICH WILL BE A LOT LESS THAN THEY GOT PAID IN LONDON...

LOOKS LIKE WIN-WIN FOR US, AGAIN!

Panel 1: THE BANK HAS HAD TO DRAG ITS BANKERS KICKING AND SCREAMING TO WORK OVER IN OUR FRANKFURT OFFICE DUE TO BREXIT.

Panel 2: NOW IRONICALLY THE WHOLE SITUATION COULD CHANGE. IF THE NEW TORY LEADER CAN'T DELIVER BREXIT IN OCTOBER HE'D HAVE TO CALL A GENERAL ELECTION...

Panel 3: A LABOUR PARTY CAMPAIGNING ON A SECOND REFERENDUM MIGHT WIN AND CANCEL BREXIT. WHERE WOULD THAT LEAVE US?

Panel 4: WE'D HAVE TO DRAG THOSE BANKERS KICKING AND SCREAMING BACK TO LONDON. SPEAK FOR YOURSELF. I'D BE JOINING THEM OUT THERE RATHER THAN HAVE TO PAY 60% INCOME TAX HERE...

Panel 1: HUAWEI PHONE SYSTEMS ARE SEEN AS PROBLEMATIC BECAUSE OF THEIR DIRECT ASSOCIATION WITH THE CHINESE COMMUNIST REGIME...

Panel 2: WHO ARE SAID TO USE INTRUSIVE TECHNOLOGY TO INTERCEPT PRIVATE CONVERSATIONS, EVEN USING ALGORITHMS THAT ARE TRIGGERED BY WORD RECOGNITION PROGRAMS.

Panel 3: IT'S A WAY OF THEM SHUTTING DOWN DISCUSSION OF SUBJECT MATTER THEY'RE SENSITIVE ABOUT... WELL, I CAN THINK OF PARTS OF THE WORLD WHERE THAT MIGHT BE A PROBLEM RIGHT NOW... HONG KONG? NO, ACTUALLY I WAS THINKING OF..

Panel 4: VACATIONS ARE GREAT HERE BUT HAWAII'S PHONE RECEPTION IS DREADFUL. YES, EVERY TIME I SAY WHERE I AM, MY PHONE CUTS OUT... YOU MENTION OUR COMPANY NAME, WE SWITCH YOU OFF, TROUBLE-MAKER... EEK!

Panel 1: AS YOUR BOSS, I KNOW IT'S TOUGH FOR YOU ANALYSTS IN THE POST-MIFID II AGE WHERE CLIENTS HAVE TO PAY FOR YOUR RESEARCH, SIMON...

Panel 2: INTENSE COMPETITION HAS DRIVEN THE MARKET RATE DOWN AND IT DOESN'T COME CLOSE TO COVERING YOUR SALARY... I CAN SEE THIS HAS LED YOU TO MAKE A SPECIAL EFFORT...

Panel 3: THIS RESEARCH NOTE YOU'VE PRODUCED IS COMPREHENSIVE, LUCID, ACCESSIBLE AND WELL-ARGUED WITH ALL DATA NEATLY PRESENTED AND A CLEAR RECOMMENDATION AT THE END...

Panel 4: SO GO BACK AND REWRITE IT; LEAVE THE CLIENT GUESSING A BIT... REMEMBER: WE NEED THEM TO BOOK IN A FACE-TO-FACE MEETING WITH YOU TO FIND OUT WHAT YOU ACTUALLY THINK ...<u>THAT'S</u> WHAT WE CAN CHARGE THE <u>REAL</u> MONEY FOR... O.K. SORRY.

Alex PEATTIE + TAYLOR

So you're going to the bank's "Women in Business" event this evening?

Yes...

It's at a top venue in the city with a female keynote speaker. All the bank's senior women will be there and we've invited all our female clients...

It's to celebrate empowerment, but it also reminds us of the disadvantages that we women still face in relation to men...

Yes...

Lots of those female clients have dropped out, which is why WE'VE been press-ganged into going along...

Well, no one wants to go to those corporate dos when the weather's nice...

It's not fair...

US BLOKES are heading for a riverside pub...

Alex PEATTIE + TAYLOR

I'm sorry, Simon, I was looking forward to meeting with you to discuss your latest investment ideas...

But under MIFID II rules we fund managers now have to pay for access to you analysts and I've just found out that you charge £5,000 for a meeting, which is over my budget...

So: sorry for the short notice but I'm going to have to downgrade our meeting to a phone call with you instead, which is cheaper... This is a bit embarrassing for me...

And for me...

I'm downstairs in your reception.

Okay, make yourself comfortable and tell me your views on China at the moment...

RECEPTION

Alex PEATTIE + TAYLOR

A charity cricket match like this gives people various ways to show their generosity...

136 FOR 3 10

Wealthy bankers and businessmen make a large contribution to the charity for the right to play in the showpiece game with cricketing legends...

WELLBEING OF WOMEN

But there are also opportunities for those who believe that charity is something that is better done quietly and unobtrusively.

Yes... like Alex.

He managed to fluff that simple catch most convincingly.

Well, his best client is batting. What else do you expect?

77

Alex PEATTIE + TAYLOR

IN THIS HIGH-PRESSURED WORK ENVIRONMENT THIS "SOCIAL ORDERING" APP WHICH ALLOWS ME TO ORDER SANDWICHES IN ADVANCE IS GREAT! I LOVE MY PHONE!

ALSO ANYONE ELSE IN OUR OFFICE WANTING A SANDWICH CAN PUT THEIR ORDERS WITH MINE SO I CAN PICK THEM ALL UP IN ONE GO WITHOUT QUEUEING..

IT BEATS THE OLD DAYS OF BEING SENT TO THE SANDWICH SHOP AND HAVING TO STAND IN LINE FOR AGES WAITING MY TURN AND WHILE THEY MADE UP THE ORDER.

BUT THINK WHAT YOU'RE MISSING, LEO....

20 MINUTES OF LEGITIMATE UNINTERRUPTED QUALITY TIME GAZING AT YOUR PERSONAL MESSAGES AND SOCIAL MEDIA ON YOUR PHONE SCREEN. YOU DON'T GET _THAT_ BACK IN THE OFFICE, DO YOU?

OH YES. BOTHER.

THE MASS REDUNDANCIES AT DEUTSCHE BANK HAVE SENT SHOCK WAVES THROUGH THE MARKET.

MEGABANK

IT'S HARDLY A GREAT ADVERTISEMENT FOR THE FINANCIAL STRENGTH OF THE EUROPEAN UNION. AND MEGABANK HAS FIRMLY NAILED ITS COLOURS TO THE REMAIN CAMP ON BREXIT...

I WONDER IF ALL THIS COULD HAVE IMPLICATIONS FOR OUR OWN FINANCIAL POSITION...

UNDOUBTEDLY...

THE MARKET IS NOW AWASH WITH BANKERS' C.V.S, SO THERE'LL BE NO NEED TO PAY OUR PEOPLE BONUSES THIS YEAR.

YOU'RE RIGHT. NO ONE WILL RISK FLOUNCING OUT IN A STROP IF THEY DON'T GET ONE...

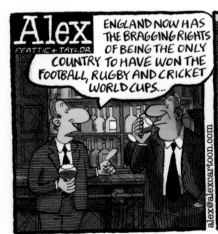

ENGLAND NOW HAS THE BRAGGING RIGHTS OF BEING THE ONLY COUNTRY TO HAVE WON THE FOOTBALL, RUGBY AND CRICKET WORLD CUPS...

WELL, I REMEMBER 1966, ALEX. I WAS THERE AT WEMBLEY WHEN ENGLAND WON THE FOOTBALL. AND I WAS IN SYDNEY IN 2003 FOR THE RUGBY VICTORY...

OF COURSE THAT WAS ALL A GOOD FEW YEARS AGO, RUPERT. THERE'S A DANGER THAT WE'RE STILL DWELLING ON PAST GLORIES..

ALL THE SAME IT WAS MARVELLOUS...

WHEN I THINK OF THE "THANK YOU" ORDERS I GOT THE NEXT DAY FROM THE CLIENTS I TOOK TO THE MATCH: A YEAR'S BUSINESS IN A DAY...

ME TOO ≋SIGH≋ BUT NO ONE MADE A PENNY OUT OF SUNDAY, THANKS TO COMPLIANCE...

WHAT A TRAGIC WASTE...

79

Alex FEATTIE + TAYLOR

THE FIRST COUNTRY ATTEMPTING TO LEAVE THE E.U. WAS ALWAYS GOING TO BE A TEST OF THE ORGANISATION'S STABILITY.

AND NOW THAT IT IS FACING THIS EXISTENTIAL THREAT, I THINK WE'RE SEEING THE RESPONSE OF THE OTHER 27 MEMBER STATES TOWARDS PRESENTING A UNIFIED FRONT...

AFTER ALL THEY'RE WELL AWARE OF THE DANGERS OF A DISORDERLY BREXIT AND WHAT IT COULD LEAD TO...

YES...

A LABOUR GOVERNMENT IN THE U.K.?

QUITE. SO THEY'RE BREAKING RANKS TO LURE OUR WEALTHY ELITE INTO TAX EXILE...

TAX BREAKS

PORTUGAL IS GIVING RESIDENCY TO PEOPLE WHO BUY A HOUSE THERE...

ITALY IS OFFERING A FLAT TAX RATE OF €100,000...

Alex FEATTIE + TAYLOR

THE MOON LANDING WAS 50 YEARS AGO THIS WEEK...

I REMEMBER IT WELL. ME AND MY FRIENDS GATHERED IN MY PARENTS' SITTING ROOM TO WATCH IT THAT MORNING...

BUT WHEN WE SAW THOSE BLURRY, FLICKERING BLACK AND WHITE PICTURES OF THE MEN FIRST SETTING FOOT ON THE LUNAR SURFACE, DO YOU KNOW WHAT MY ABIDING THOUGHT WAS?

WHAT?

I THOUGHT: IS THIS IT? WHAT A WASTE. WHAT A HUGE, COLOSSAL WASTE OF RESOURCES AND TECHNOLOGY AND HUMAN ENTERPRISE.... WHAT A WASTE OF MONEY...

REALLY?

YES. WE WERE ONE OF THE FIRST FAMILIES IN THE NEIGHBOURHOOD TO HAVE A COLOUR TV, BUT IT WASN'T GOING TO IMPRESS ANYONE WITH THAT FOOTAGE ON IT...

Alex FEATTIE + TAYLOR

SO YOU THINK WE SHOULD BE ADVISING OUR CLIENTS IN NORTHERN IRELAND ABOUT THE BACK STOP, ALEX?

I DO. YES.

WE NEED TO GO AND CONVINCE BUSINESSES THERE THAT THEY DON'T NEED TO WORRY ABOUT THEIR STATUS AS PART OF THE UNITED KINGDOM...

AND AT THE SAME TIME THAT THEY CAN RELY ON THE ADVANTAGES OF TRADING ACROSS BORDERS THAT ARE NEITHER HARD NOR CLOSED...

EXACTLY...

THE TWO KEYWORDS TO BE STRESSED HERE ARE "BRITISH" AND "OPEN"...

THANK YOU, CLIVE, THAT MAKES IT VERY CLEAR...

CLICK

OF COURSE! THE GOLF IS ON THERE NOW AND YOU TWO WANT TO GO WATCH IT...

WAS THAT SOME KIND OF FREUDIAN SLIP, CLIVE?

IDIOT, CLIVE.

BRITISH OPEN

SORRY, ALEX.

81

Alex PEATTIE + TAYLOR

WHY ARE MILLENNIALS SO FIT?

THEY HAVE DIFFERENT VALUES TO US. THEY KNOW THEY WON'T GET MORTGAGES, AND THE GLORY DAYS OF THE CITY ARE OVER...

OUR GENERATION WAS MUCH MORE MATERIALISTIC. THE WHOLE ETHOS WAS STRIVING FOR MORE MONEY, STATUS SYMBOLS, ASSETS AND BETTER-PAID JOBS. BUT THOSE TIMES ARE GONE...

INSTEAD, THE YOUNG FOCUS ON LIFE EXPERIENCES LIKE TRAVEL, AND WORKING ON THEIR GYM-HONED BODIES TO LOOK GOOD...

SO WHEN THEY WANT TO BLAG A PAY RISE OUT OF THEIR BOSS TO PREVENT THEM GOING OFF SOMEWHERE ELSE, THEY LOOK LIKE THEY'RE GETTING THEIR "BEACH BODIES" READY TO TAKE ANOTHER GAP YEAR...

AH... INSTEAD OF HINTING THEY MIGHT DEFECT TO ANOTHER BANK, LIKE WE USED TO... I SEE...

Alex PEATTIE + TAYLOR

WE MAY DISPARAGE MILLENNIALS, BUT THEY'RE ACTUALLY QUITE PRINCIPLED AND IDEALISTIC...

THEY GENUINELY BELIEVE IN ETHICAL INVESTING, E.S.G. POLICIES, COMBATTING CLIMATE CHANGE ETC... AND THOSE WHO COME TO WORK IN THE CITY FEEL THEY CAN MAKE A DIFFERENCE...

THOUGH OBVIOUSLY WHEN IT COMES TO PERSUADING LARGE CORPORATIONS TO MAKE MAJOR POLICY CHANGES YOU HAVE TO ASK HOW MUCH POWER A JUNIOR BANKER HAS...

QUITE A LOT: THEY'RE ALL THE CHILDREN OF CLIENTS. WELL HOW ELSE WOULD THEY HAVE GOT A JOB HERE?

I'M LOBBYING MY DAD TO STOP HIM USING PALM OIL IN HIS MULTINATIONAL.

Alex PEATTIE + TAYLOR

SO, JUSTIN, YOU'VE RESIGNED AS A MINISTER FROM THE GOVERNMENT?

YES, MY VIEWS WERE NOT IN KEEPING WITH THE NEW PM'S STANCE ON BREXIT.

AS AN EX-BANKER MYSELF I CAN CLEARLY SEE HOW DAMAGING AND COSTLY TO THE BUSINESS COMMUNITY A NO DEAL BREXIT ON THE 31ST OCTOBER WOULD BE...

NOW I BELIEVE THE BEST HOPE IS THAT WE FIND SOME WAY TO DELAY BREXIT BEYOND THE 3-MONTH DEADLINE. THE THREE MONTHS BEFORE THE WITHDRAWAL DATE?

ER, I MEANT THE THREE MONTH RULE AFTER WHICH I'M ALLOWED TO GET A JOB ONCE I'VE LEFT OFFICE... THEN I CAN BECOME A CONSULTANT ADVISING COMPANIES ON THEIR NO DEAL STRATEGY...

AH! LUCRATIVE...

I'M CROSSING MY FINGERS...

Alex PEATTIE + TAYLOR

YOU OLD-SCHOOL FUND MANAGERS DON'T SEEM TO UNDERSTAND YOUR REGULATORY RESPONSIBILITIES THESE DAYS...

YOU WERE USED TO BEING LAVISHLY ENTERTAINED BY ALL THE BROKERS WITHOUT HAVING TO PROVIDE ANY JUSTIFICATION TO US IN THE COMPLIANCE DEPARTMENT.

BUT NOW YOU MUST LOG ON OUR SYSTEM FULL DETAILS OF ANY EVENT YOU ARE INVITED TO, INCLUDING THOSE YOU DECLINE, STATING YOUR REASON FOR DOING SO...

I DID ALL THAT... LOOK...

IT WAS THE LESS PRESTIGIOUS OPERA AT GLYNDEBOURNE, WITH THE SECOND-TIER CAST, DINNER AT THE INFERIOR RESTAURANT AND AT SHORT NOTICE, WHICH IMPLIED I WASN'T FIRST CHOICE...

NEXT TIME JUST STICK TO SAYING THAT IT WOULD HAVE CONTRAVENED THE BRIBERY ACT...

Alex PEATTIE + TAYLOR

SO HERE WE ARE HAVING BREAKFAST TOGETHER, ALEX...

THE WOLSELEY

YES, CAPPUCCINO AND CROISSANTS. IT'S IRONIC, MIKE...

LUNCH OR DINNER USED TO BE THE OCCASIONS FOR GETTING TOGETHER WITH ONE'S CONTACTS, BUT THE MODERN WORKING DAY SEEMS TO BE EXPANDING TO ENCROACH FURTHER INTO ONE'S PERSONAL TIME...

TRUE.

YOU JUST HAVE TO ASK YOURSELF IF THE TWO OF US WOULD HAVE BEEN MEETING UP AT THIS UNGODLY HOUR OF THE MORNING TWENTY YEARS AGO...

THAT GOES WITHOUT SAYING...

OF COURSE: WE'D BE HAVING A HAIR-OF-THE-DOG AT 6 A.M. IN THE ALL-NIGHT SMITHFIELD MEAT PORTERS' PUB AFTER A HEAVY NIGHT ON THE TILES WHEN WE'D ENDED UP SLEEPING IN OUR OFFICES...

THOSE WERE THE DAYS...

Alex PEATTIE + TAYLOR

fringe

WHILE WE'RE IN EDINBURGH WE SHOULD CATCH OUR EX-CLIENT TRISTRAM'S STAND-UP SHOW...

HE'S PERFORMING UP HERE?

YES, WE RIDICULED HIM AT THE TRY-OUT NIGHTS HE DID IN GROTTY COMEDY CLUBS IN NORTH LONDON, BUT THIS COULD MEAN WE HAVE TO START TAKING HIM SERIOUSLY AS A COMEDIAN. YOU RECKON?

DON'T FORGET, CLIVE, EDINBURGH HAS A VERY HIGH INTERNATIONAL PRESTIGE IN THE WORLD HE'S TRYING TO MAKE A LIVING IN...

STAND-UP COMEDY?

ER, NO, FINANCE. I HEAR HE'S ALSO SEEING HEADHUNTERS UP HERE TO GET HIMSELF A NEW JOB..

OH NO... IF HE SUCCEEDS WE'LL HAVE TO START LAUGHING AT HIS JOKES AGAIN TO GET HIS BUSINESS...

Alex PEATTIE + TAYLOR

WE CAME TO EDINBURGH TO SEE TRISTRAM'S ACT BUT THERE ARE PLENTY MORE COMICS ON THE SAME BILL...

BOX OFFICE

QUEUE HERE

AS MIDDLE-AGED BANKERS WE DO RATHER STAND OUT FROM THE CROWD, BUT ALEX SAYS IT'S WORTH IT TO HEAR WHAT YOUNG STAND-UPS HAVE TO SAY...

HE SAYS IF YOU LIKE TO BE CHALLENGED AND YOU'RE NOT EASILY OFFENDED THERE'S ONLY ONE PLACE TO BE: HERE AT THE COMEDY CLUB, AT THE HEAD OF THE QUEUE...

THEN RIGHT IN THE FRONT ROW WHERE YOU GET PICKED ON

OH! WE'VE GOT A <u>BANKER</u> IN THE AUDIENCE! YOU'RE AN OVERPAID, OVER-PRIVILEGED, RUTHLESS, AMORAL, MATERIALISTIC B*ST*RD...

I KNOW!

I BET YOU'VE GOT A PORSCHE DON'T YOU?!

HA! <u>TWO!</u>

=PREEN=

Alex PEATTIE + TAYLOR

SO YOU KNOW THIS STAND-UP?

YES. HE USED TO WORK IN THE CITY OF LONDON WITH ME...

REALLY? WELL HE'S GOT A VERY SOUGHT-AFTER LATE NIGHT SLOT.

YES. HE'S WELL-REGARDED ON THE COMEDY CIRCUIT THESE DAYS...

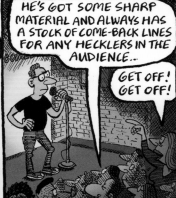

HE'S GOT SOME SHARP MATERIAL AND ALWAYS HAS A STOCK OF COME-BACK LINES FOR ANY HECKLERS IN THE AUDIENCE...

GET OFF! GET OFF!

AH, THAT'S MY WIFE... REMINDING ME THAT I'VE GOT A BREAKFAST MEETING WITH A HEADHUNTER TOMORROW...

IT REALLY <u>IS</u>... HE'S DESPERATE TO GET BACK INTO THE FINANCIAL WORLD...

I WON'T BE LONG, DARLING.

Alex PEATTIE + TAYLOR

SO YOU'RE ENJOYING TRISTRAM'S EDIN-BURGH FESTIVAL SHOW...

YES, HE'S TAILORED HIS MATERIAL...

HE'S IN SCOTLAND NOW AND HIS AUDIENCE IS MAINLY YOUNGER PEOPLE AND THEY TEND TO BE IN FAVOUR OF MEMBERSHIP OF THE EUROPEAN UNION, BUT AGAINST SCOTLAND'S UNION WITH ENGLAND.

SO HE'S ADOPTED A MORE PRO-E.U., PRO-SCOTTISH INDEPENDENCE STANCE, WHICH MAKES SENSE WHEN YOU THINK THAT HE'S TRYING TO APPEAL TO PEOPLE UP HERE.

TO GET HIMSELF A JOB IN A BANK? SO IF SCOTLAND VOTES FOR INDEP-ENDENCE POST-BREXIT AND STAYS IN THE E.U. THEN ALL LONDON'S BUSINESS COULD MOVE <u>HERE</u>...

RIGHT. AND WE'D NEED TO SUCK UP TO HIM. TO GET <u>US</u> JOBS...

SO START LAUGHING...

alex@alexcartoon.com

Also available from Masterley Publishing

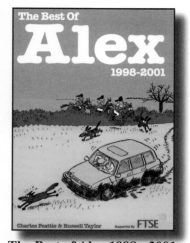

The Best of Alex 1998 - 2001
Boom to bust via the dotcom bubble.

The Best of Alex 2002
Scandals rock the corporate world.

The Best of Alex 2003
Alex gets made redundant.

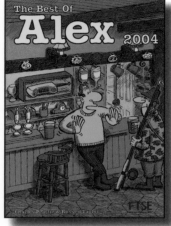

The Best of Alex 2004
And gets his job back.

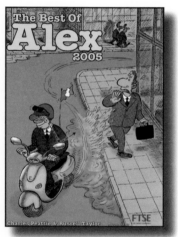

The Best of Alex 2005
Alex has problems with the French.

The Best of Alex 2006
Alex gets a new American boss.

The Best of Alex 2007
Alex restructures Christmas.

The Best of Alex 2008
The credit crunch bites

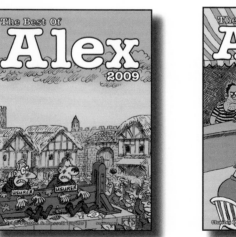

The Best of Alex 2009
Global capitalism self-destructs.

The Best of Alex 2010
Somehow the City lurches on.

The Best of Alex 2011
The financial crisis continues.

The Best of Alex 2012
The Olympics come to London.

The Best of Alex 2013
It's a wonderful crisis.

The Best of Alex 2014
The 'New Normal' takes hold.

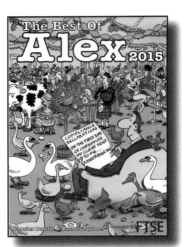

The Best of Alex 2015
Compliance rules the roost.

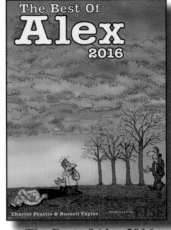

The Best of Alex 2016
Alex battles Brexit and Bitcoin.

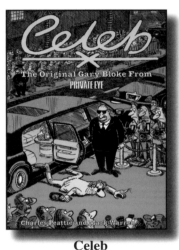

Celeb
Wrinkly rock star Gary Bloke.

The Best of Alex 2017
30 years in the City and counting...

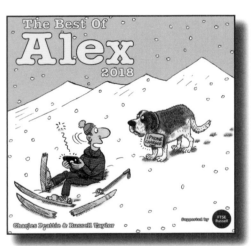

The Best of Alex 2018
Brexit and more Brexit...